Laugh-a-LOT!
ALPHA...

My Little Workbook

ISBN: 978-1-5461-2667-6

Art Director: Tannaz Fassihi; Designer: Tanya Chernyak; Illustrated by Kevin Zimmer and Michael Robertson; Copyright © Liza Charlesworth.
All rights reserved. Published by Scholastic Inc.

1 2 3 4 5 6 7 8 9 10   68   33 32 31 30 29 28 27 26 25 24

Made in Jiaxing, China. First printing, May 2024.

SCHOLASTIC INC.

Contents

Book-by-Book Practice Pages

Dear Learner:

This little workbook is here to give you extra practice with the alphabet. Turn to it each time you complete a new book in this set. Doing the activities will help you learn your letters from A to Z and prepare you to become a super-strong reader.

Happy Learning!
Your Friends at Scholastic

Alphabet Mascot Chart

Use this chart to quickly reference each primary letter sound from A to Z.

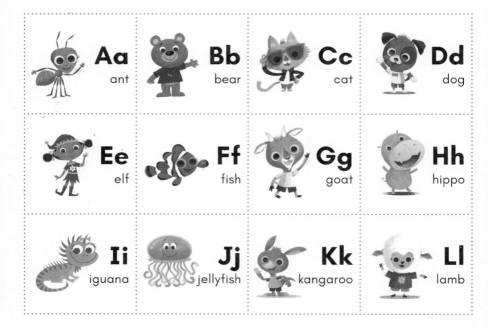

Aa ant

Bb bear

Cc cat

Dd dog

Ee elf

Ff fish

Gg goat

Hh hippo

Ii iguana

Jj jellyfish

Kk kangaroo

Ll lamb

 **Mm**
monster

 Nn
newt

 **Oo**
octopus

 Pp
pig

 Qq
queen

 **Rr**
robot

 Ss
seal

 Tt
tiger

 **Uu**
umbrella

 **Vv**
vegetables

 **Ww**
walrus

 Xx
fox

 **Yy**
yak

 Zz
zebra

Now I know my A-B-Cs, next time won't you sing with me? ♪♪

5

Aa

Trace, then write big A and little a.

Shade in each box with big A or little a.

A	d	a	E	k	A
C	a	f	A	a	i
G	p	O	A	a	J
a	R	q	N	L	A

Fill in the blank. Then, draw a picture to go with your response.

> ## My favorite thing that begins with the letter a is
>
> _____.

Bb

Trace, then write big B and little b.

B B

b b

Shade in each box with big B or little b.

A	B	a	E	j	B
b	G	f	B	b	b
H	p	b	A	i	K
B	r	B	N	b	D

Fill in the blank. Then, draw a picture to go with your response.

My favorite thing that begins with the letter b is

_____.

Cc

Trace, then write big C and little c.

C C

C C

Shade in each box with big C or little c.

C	O	c	e	c	B
j	c	f	c	C	n
s	p	C	A	i	C
C	r	T	c	m	d

Laugh-a-Lot Alphabet © Scholastic Inc. • page 10

Fill in the blank. Then, draw a picture to go with your response.

> **My favorite thing that begins with the letter c is**
>
> _____.

Dd

Trace, then write big D and little d.

D D

d d

Shade in each box with big D or little d.

D	w	d	e	c	B
x	D	f	d	D	d
R	H	d	A	i	D
D	m	T	d	d	z

Fill in the blank. Then, draw a picture to go with your response.

My favorite thing that begins with the letter d is

_____.

Ee

Trace, then write big E and little e.

E E

e

Shade in each box with big E or little e.

e	w	E	e	c	Y
Z	e	f	d	E	a
v	i	E	o	i	e
E	J	k	E	e	L

Fill in the blank. Then, draw a picture to go with your response.

My favorite thing that begins with the letter e is

_____.

Ff

Trace, then write big F and little f.

Shade in each box with big F or little f.

C	w	E	f	u	Z
F	F	e	B	a	f
V	i	f	F	i	F
f	J	f	b	F	y

Fill in the blank. Then, draw a picture to go with your response.

> **My favorite thing that begins with the letter f is**
>
> _____.

Gg

Trace, then write big G and little g.

Shade in each box with big G or little g.

E	w	G	g	Z	o
g	G	e	g	a	G
w	c	G	F	i	g
X	g	a	G	u	B

Fill in the blank. Then, draw a picture to go with your response.

My favorite thing that begins with the letter g is

_____.

Hh

Trace, then write big H and little h.

Shade in each box with big H or little h.

H	C	P	h	Z	H
r	h	e	H	q	n
l	A	h	F	H	O
h	H	f	s	h	g

Fill in the blank. Then, draw a picture to go with your response.

My favorite thing that begins with the letter h is

_____.

Ii

Trace, then write big I and little i.

Shade in each box with big I or little i.

i	w	P	h	x	i
Q	I	e	i	i	z
l	u	i	b	I	O
y	i	f	I	W	I

Fill in the blank. Then, draw a picture to go with your response.

My favorite thing that begins with the letter i is

_____.

Jj

Trace, then write big J and little j.

Shade in each box with big J or little j.

i	G	j	c	J	i
J	j	e	j	a	J
l	h	i	j	J	p
j	J	K	I	n	j

Fill in the blank. Then, draw a picture to go with your response.

My favorite thing that begins with the letter j is

_____.

Kk

Trace, then write big K and little k.

K K

k k

Shade in each box with big K or little k.

i	G	j	k	e	A
K	k	r	h	K	d
l	K	i	B	K	k
k	q	K	k	m	j

Fill in the blank. Then, draw a picture to go with your response.

My favorite thing that begins with the letter k is

_____.

Trace, then write big L and little l.

Shade in each box with big L or little l.

l	p	j	L	d	A
k	l	L	b	i	l
l	L	B	l	L	u
L	S	l	k	v	G

Fill in the blank. Then, draw a picture to go with your response.

> **My favorite thing that begins with the letter l is**
>
> _____.

Mm

Trace, then write big M and little m.

Shade in each box with big M or little m.

E	m	j	x	d	M
M	l	a	m	m	U
o	M	B	i	M	u
m	S	M	y	W	m

Mm

Fill in the blank. Then, draw a picture to go with your response.

> **My favorite thing that begins with the letter m is**
>
> _____ .

Nn

Trace, then write big N and little n.

N N

n n

Shade in each box with big N or little n.

a	m	c	N	G	n
n	o	N	J	n	U
Z	n	C	i	e	N
N	S	n	k	N	e

Fill in the blank. Then, draw a picture to go with your response.

My favorite thing that begins with the letter n is

_____.

Oo

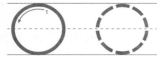

Trace, then write big O and little o.

Shade in each box with big O or little o.

o	h	c	u	G	O
n	O	N	o	o	x
O	n	o	i	e	O
s	W	o	O	f	Y

Fill in the blank. Then, draw a picture to go with your response.

My favorite thing that begins with the letter o is

_____.

Pp

Trace, then write big P and little p.

Shade in each box with big P or little p.

a	S	P	n	G	p
P	m	p	i	P	o
x	h	J	p	e	P
p	S	P	k	p	M

Fill in the blank. Then, draw a picture to go with your response.

My favorite thing that begins with the letter p is

_____.

Qq

Trace, then write big Q and little q.

Shade in each box with big Q or little q.

q	S	c	N	G	q
p	Q	q	m	Q	i
T	a	U	q	e	Q
Q	j	P	Q	q	w

Fill in the blank. Then, draw a picture to go with your response.

My favorite thing that begins with the letter q is

_____.

Rr

Trace, then write big R and little r.

R R

r r

Shade in each box with big R or little r.

r	x	E	R	h	Z
b	R	z	r	Q	r
v	r	R	c	R	f
r	W	P	R	q	A

Fill in the blank. Then, draw a picture to go with your response.

> **My favorite thing that begins with the letter r is**
>
> _____.

Ss

Trace, then write big S and little s.

S S

s s

Shade in each box with big S or little s.

s	Y	S	R	o	x
D	s	b	S	r	S
Z	S	R	s	T	s
S	h	P	s	v	j

Fill in the blank. Then, draw a picture to go with your response.

> ## My favorite thing that begins with the letter s is
>
> _____.

Trace, then write big T and little t.

Shade in each box with big T or little t.

t	a	N	T	i	C
T	S	t	o	t	T
x	u	R	q	s	z
t	W	T	t	e	T

Fill in the blank. Then, draw a picture to go with your response.

My favorite thing that begins with the letter t is

_____.

Uu

Trace, then write big U and little u.

Shade in each box with big U or little u.

U	O	u	J	E	u
v	X	u	r	U	b
x	u	s	u	m	U
U	W	T	U	i	w

Fill in the blank. Then, draw a picture to go with your response.

My favorite thing that begins with the letter u is

_____.

Vv

Trace, then write big V and little v.

Shade in each box with big V or little v.

U	o	V	m	V	u
v	z	W	r	v	V
x	v	s	E	k	v
V	G	V	v	G	a

Fill in the blank. Then, draw a picture to go with your response.

> ## My favorite thing that begins with the letter v is
>
> _____.

Ww

Trace, then write big W and little w.

W W

W W

Shade in each box with big W or little w.

e	w	V	J	V	W
w	z	W	N	i	m
W	w	s	w	W	v
x	G	h	w	u	W

Fill in the blank. Then, draw a picture to go with your response.

My favorite thing that begins with the letter w is

_____.

Trace, then write big X and little x.

Shade in each box with big X or little x.

o	x	V	k	X	N
w	Z	X	a	i	x
X	S	d	x	X	U
x	b	X	g	L	x

Fill in the blank. Then, draw a picture to go with your response.

My favorite thing that ends with the letter x is

_____.

Yy

Trace, then write big Y and little y.

Shade in each box with big Y or little y.

Y	y	e	Y	i	y
a	C	y	G	y	x
Y	Y	f	u	X	B
b	D	y	q	o	Y

Fill in the blank. Then, draw a picture to go with your response.

My favorite thing that begins with the letter y is

_____.

Zz

Trace, then write big Z and little z.

Shade in each box with big Z or little z.

b	Z	z	Y	i	Z
S	r	y	h	Z	n
z	o	G	Z	x	z
Z	D	z	A	z	d

Fill in the blank. Then, draw a picture to go with your response.

> **My favorite thing that begins with the letter z is**
>
> _____.

Letter Sound Review

Draw lines to connect the letters to pictures that begin with them.

Aa

Bb

Cc

Dd

Letter Sound Review

Draw lines to connect the letters to pictures that begin with them.

Ee

Ff

Gg

Hh

5

Letter Sound Review

Draw lines to connect the letters to pictures that begin with them.

Ii

Jj

Kk

Ll

Letter Sound Review

Draw lines to connect the letters to pictures that begin with them.

Mm

Nn

Oo

Pp

Letter Sound Review

Draw lines to connect the letters to pictures that begin with them.

Qq

Rr

Ss

Tt

Uu

Letter Sound Review

Draw lines to connect the letters to pictures that begin or end *(six)* with them.

Vv

Ww

Xx

Yy

Zz

CONGRATULATIONS!

_____
child's name

The kid named here
is as cool as can be
and knows every letter
from A to Z!